Tatterlegs f
Tea

To my wife, Shirley

The pee-wits cry at dawn
Across the frosty air,
In my bed I'm warm
And life is good, for you are there.

Catterlegs for Tea

more Suffolk Dialect in Tales and Verse
from

David Woodward

illustrated by

Rosemary Brown

Nostalgia Publications

TOFTWOOD ◦ DEREHAM ◦ NORFOLK ◦ NR19 1NB

Published by:
NOSTALGIA PUBLICATIONS
(Terry Davy)
7 Elm Park, Toftwood,
Dereham, Norfolk,
NR19 1NB

First Impression: October 1998

© David Woodward (text) and Rosemary Brown
(illustrations) 1998

ISBN 0 947630 20 1

Design and Typesetting:
NOSTALGIA PUBLICATIONS

Printed by:
PAGE BROS. (NORWICH) LTD.
Mile Cross Lane,
Norwich,
Norfolk NR6 6SA

Contents

Acknowledgements

Thanks to Terry Davy for publishing this book, and to Rosemary Brown for her apt and excellent illustrations. Also to Nick Patrick of BBC Radio Suffolk for writing the Foreword (I still owe him a pint!).

Bob White's *Ole Ephraim* has had chuckles rippling along the Waveney Valley delighting readers of the Sheaf and Waveney Life Magazines. I am privileged in having Bob's permission to include some of his yarns.

Thanks to Brian Patrick for his *November* poems and to Jean Kinge who wrote *Autumn in Suffolk*.

We are indebted to Katherine Makower and Susan Meek, neices of the late Cecil Lay of Aldringham, who readily agreed to my request to include their uncle's poem *"To Suffolk"*.

My son Michael and Treeza Sodah, aided by my wife Shirley and Jo Pigot, have all helped in research and preparation. Mary Durrant has reminded me of war-time memories. My cousin, Michael Woodward, vividly recalled his time spent in Suffolk as an evacuee.

But once again, "Thank yer kindly, all on yer tergether" who have joined me in sharing Suffolk memories.

Sea Kale at Sizewell

Foreword

Those that listen to BBC Radio Suffolk at dinnertime during the week are probably of the opinion that my life revolves round the village boozer. Well, in some ways I suppose it does. Not just for the beer though. I'm quite happy to while away an evening 'sittin on a pinta Adnums' watching the intricacies of Phat and smiling at the wonderful wit that flows from bar to bar. What does this have to do with the follow up to the very popular *Larn Yarself Silly Suffolk*? Well let me tell you …

I was 'up the Buck' one night and out of the half light of the back bar came a little 'ole boy' with tangled white hair and a mischievous twinkle in his eye. 'There's summut you can do for me boy', he half whispered, leaning towards me and nudging my side with his elbow. Not used to seeing him in the particular hostelry, it took me a few seconds to realise it was the author. It could easily have been the local blacksmith or wheelwright, were they still in business. But then David Woodward's craft has a skill that they would have instantly recognised.

I'm none too sure who reads Forewords these days, but now you have got this far let me tell you of the treat that awaits you over the page. *Tatterlegs for Tea* is a warm mix of some of the essential qualities of the Suffolk character, superb observation, humour, appreciation of the past and poetic understanding of the present.

Nick Patrick
BBC Radio Suffolk,
1998

Introduction

Thank you to all the folks - South Folks and way beyond - who decided to read *Larn Yourself Silly Suffolk*. The format for this type of book was set by *Larn Yarself Norfolk,* and it has proved a winner. Northamptonshire is the next County to benefit. I hope, nay I am sure, it will only be the third in a growing series.

Terry Davy asked me in early 1998 to produce a follow-up to the book on Suffolk dialect. "But keep it in the same style" he said. "Bring characters, customs, old remedies and sayings in" - and he made it sound so simple. Most publishers do, I have since been told. Two things soon happened that made writing this book a joy.

First I heard that Rosemary Brown, the daughter of Mary Brown who so ably illustrated *Larn Yourself Silly Suffolk,* was to be the illustrator. So whatever I wrote, the book was on course from the start. Her feelings for Suffolk encapsulate fully my written thoughts.

But how do I get all the ideas, sayings and characters portrayed in an entertaining form, I pondered? My wife, Shirley, came up with the solution. From her idea I have been able to produce a format. Her suggestion was simple yet clever. Why hadn't I thought of it? But what do we have these little ole mawthers for? "You tell stories and write verse that audiences of all ages enjoy and your Suffolk accent and dialect is to the fore. Base the book around that theme." I have done so and this book is dedicated to her.

Finally, since the Suffolk dictionary was published in *Larn Yourself Silly Suffolk* last year, so many people have written, telephoned, stopped me in the street or around the shops. They enquired why I did not mention a

8

particular word or asked if I had heard a certain idiom or saying. I have tried in the past year to foster this interest and I have been provided with several more ideas. So to keep the interest in the dialect alive and continuing, another look at Suffolk's language, customs and idioms can be found in the early part of the book.

We hope that you will enjoy reading this volume as much as Rosemary, Terry and I have enjoyed preparing it for publication.

How I Kept On A' Larnin

Since I wrote *Larn Yourself Silly Suffolk* in 1997 I have been pleased to receive many comments from people about their own observations on the dialect and idioms of Suffolk. The more you delve into the history of Suffolk and East Anglian speech you realise how much there is to learn and discover. It would be possible to spend your whole life studying our dialect and traditions of oral history and at the end there would be still more to discover.

There can often be more than one idea for the meaning and reasons for the use of different words. Let me give two examples.

1: Mardle

I have always thought that the word "mardle", meaning to indulge in idle gossip, derived from a dialect word for the village pond. In the olden days it would have been the focal point for village life, where all the local chat took place. So the name for a pond, "mardle" also became the dialect word for gossip. Keith Skipper in his *Larn Yourself Norfolk* came to the same conclusion. As did the much respected Suffolk historian the late George Ewart Evans.

I thought that the word was very East Anglian. I have, as yet, not found it in any of my readings about dialects beyond East Anglia or in asking folk from foreign parts.

Listening to the "Today" programme a year or so ago I was amazed to hear one of the presenters, a Scot, when he wanted to stop the light hearted banter between interviews, say "Enough of this mardling, we must get on with the next topic." Did the word mardle therefore have a wider use than East Anglian? It crossed

A good old mardle by the village duck pond

my mind that it might have been taken beyond the region by the numerous cattle drovers travelling to this area from the Highlands and the Shires. As their regular stops would be at village ponds, they would soon discover what it was to have a good old mardle.

Drovers figure in two pieces of literature. Sir Walter Scott wrote a short story about them but of greater Suffolk significance, our poet Robert Bloomfield (1766-1823) wrote a "Song for a Highland Drover - Returning from England."

"To the mountains away; my heart bounds like the hind;

For home is so sweet, and my Maggy so kind."

What an easy, simple yet charming way for a dialect word to cross the regions.

During the past year, to my amazement, I came across another idea for the reason that gossip became a "mardle". In 1949 the Eastern Daily Press published a book entitled *Broad Norfolk*. It had a lovely picture of a Suffolk Punch at the farriers on the front cover! The introduction to the book was written by Jonathan Mardle. Ironically, his writing was never idle chat but topical essays of superb quality.

In a letter to the Eastern Daily Press in 1949 the Reverend H. F. Rushmer of Oxborough wrote that he had been told "mardle" came from the "small talks" of women engaged in the process of mardling in the work of Flemish weavers preparing their fabrics.

The Rev. Brewer's classic edition of *"A Dictionary of Phrase and Fable"* (1894) is quite definite. Mardle: to waste time in gossip. (Anglo-Saxon methelian-to talk, methel-a discourse).

2: Paigle

Since last year the word Paigle has given me some cause for thought. I was sure that it was the dialect word for cowslip. And from this arose paigle or cowslip wine. The East Anglian writer Harold Freeman uses the term and a

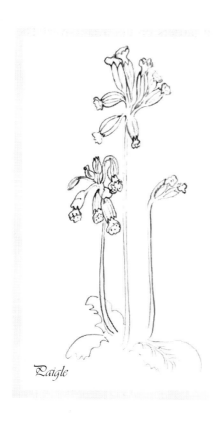

Paigle

friend told me his mother made paigle wine from cowslips in the 1920's.

In his delightful account of Cambridgeshire village life, *Journal of a Country Parish,* Robin Page writes, "warm weather never sets in until the 'paigles' (cowslips) are finished," thus confirming my understanding of the word and the fact some words extend beyond our Suffolk borders.

An old school friend, now living in Cambridge, also found some locals who knew the word. But friends from Hertfordshire and London had no knowledge.

Then around mid-summer last year I was driving with a friend whose roots are deeply set in mid-Suffolk clay. The marshes we viewed from the Gillingham Dam looked sinister. Men dressed in white boots, suits and hooded helmets like spacemen were standing around a huge tractor attached to a massive piece of spraying equipment. The booms on the sprayer looked as wide as the wings on a "Flying Fortress". The noxious smell of the spray filled the car. My friend remarked, "they are spraying the ole paigles."

"Blas'," I thought, "Have I got it wrong?" It was obvious he was referring to buttercups.

So further enquiries have continued in the past year. W. G. Munnings, again writing to the Eastern Daily Press in 1949, suggests in East Anglia there are two very similar dialect words, "peagle" - for creeping buttercup and "pagle" for cowslip. Both different to my paigle but similar enough to cause confusion. But paigle/pagle for cowslip seems safe, and maybe we ought to add peagle for creeping buttercup!

Another word, **daag** or **dayg** for dew or mist, I regret not including in my dictionary last year. No excuse for this for one of the first poems I was asked to read in the dialect starts: "A hivvy dayg 'usmornin' that woz."

Written by H. C. Buxton and entitled "Spring in the Air", I was delighted to come across it again in an East Anglian magazine of 1963 whilst at the Ipswich Record Office last year. Another correspondent also mentions the word, spelling it "Dag" and describing it as the morning mist. He said he thought it had Swedish origins.

Buttercup

14

Also mentioned have been the following words which readers will find of interest and be able to make their own local comparisons.

Scud - the mist off the sea. The Oxford English Dictionary defines one of the meanings as vapoury driving clouds. Not quite the same as the use of the word in Suffolk.

Duller - noise or cry of pain, from the Welsh "Dulyn", melancholy. The word is definitely also used in Norfolk. There is a line in John Ketts poem, "Aylsham Sale", "Listen to the dullor". Again the word is spelt slightly differently, an indication that dialect comes from an oral tradition and when written can vary in locations and manuscripts.

Hick along - to limp or propel yourself on scooter or with one foot on a cycle pedal, from the Danish "Hinke" to limp.

Swangways - cross-ways. I was overjoyed to hear the word used by my Paigle friend. We were unloading a trailer load of cord wood. Two or three pieces got out of true in the pile. He advised not to let too many go swangways. I had never heard the word in conversation before. Both my informers are Suffolk born but from quite different parts of the county.

Palarvarins - is used in this part of Suffolk for making excuses.

Drift is a driveway

One wonders why most areas will have unusual pronunciations. Covert in Frostenden was always **Covey**. Villagers always talk of Square Covey and Covey Lane.

Guildhall Lane is always **Guy-all** Lane. Quite a lot of people were suddenly aware of the strange local pronunciation when they saw it in print as Guildhall. It would be interesting to learn how many of these obscure pronunciations occur in the different Suffolk parishes.

Heater or **Hetter** - must also be added to our list of words. My little ole mawther Shirley still uses it in conversation and loves doing so. Recently she remarked how tall the grass had grown on the hetter on Clay Common in our village. The term derives from the shape of the

Grass on the Heater
or Hetter

small plot of land at road junctions on minor roads. Their triangular shape is just like the old fashioned pressing irons or heaters warmed on a fire trivet or stove in the olden days.

The Morphrey or Morphrudite was constructed by using the farm tumbril, a two-wheeled cart used in the winter and autumn for carting sugar-beet, mangolds or muck. Two extra wheels, shafts and a platform were attached in front of the tumbril, making a longer cart. This enabled large loads of hay or corn sheaves to be collected from the field.

The name derives from *Hermaphrodite:* person, plant, animal with characteristics of both sexes.

Another correspondent who was born in Lowestoft and now lives near Stowmarket informed me his Grandmother used to say: **"Don't be so ickery"**, when they were irritable or awkward. Although the word was not heard often it linked with the Iceni in whose territory Lowestoft was. He can also remember his Grandmother calling to the baker at the door with a basket of bread. "I'll be there **drecly**" - directly.

Yarmouth folk use **sulky** or **suky** and **leery** for strange or awkward. This reminded me that I remember **leery** being used when I was at school in Suffolk.

I was also informed during the year that the word **scrammed** was used in the Felixstowe area as meaning chilled with cold. But in this case there was a possibility it may have been imported from Dorset. Does any reader know?

The **ransacker** called to repair fishing nets. The **"look 'em up man"** was the rag and bone man. Both terms now out of use. Other sayings told me which are self explanatory include: **"You ought to be found out and spoke about Bor!"** and **"You can't put it where it aint!"** **"He is two slates short on the roof."** Also, **"It's all the go.":** Popular, everybody doing it. **"Large morning"**: a form of greeting on a fine bright morning.

A phrase I had never heard before, but led to much interest and amusement when I visited

Sotterley Ladies Guild, was: **"Hold yah booky low gal!"** This was advice given to a bride who was already 'expecting' on her wedding day. Holding the bouquet low prevented the congregation being aware of her state.

The Suffolk poet, Robert Bloomfield (1766-1823) used the dialect in his poem, The Horkey (Harvest Supper). Here are some examples:

Sitch a mort, a good number.

A shanny-pated crew, careless, thoughtless. I can remember my parents using the term about people not held in very high regard. "It's no good relying on him, he's a bit shanny".

Skriggled, to try and relieve yourself from the clutch of someone:

"They skriggled and began to scold
But laughing got the master;
Some quack'ling cried 'let go your hold',
The farmer's held the faster."

For the nonce, for the purpose - is also used by Bloomfield in his work, but it is a word not in dialect use in my lifetime.

Likewise another word, **Kedge,** meaning to feel sprightly and youthful in spite of advancing years:

"I'm surely growing young again;
I feel myself so kedge and plump.
From head to foot I've not one pain;
Nay hang me if I couldn't jump."

To Suffolk   Cecil Lay (1885-1956)

When mavises began to build,
And lilac twigs again were filled;
When buds had thickened in the glen,
And ducks in couples sought the fen,
When sticklebacks were rosy-gilled,
And blackthorn blanched petals spilled;
When frogs were stirring in the mud,
And chestnuts sticky in the bud;
Said I, when night shall equal day,
From winter quarters I'll away.

When robins fed their spotted young,
And catkins from the hazels hung;
When warbler flaunting warbler sung,
And squirrels on the pine-trees rung;
When days were bright, and skies were blue,
And yokels 'gan again to woo,
When thrush and blackbird early woke,
And leaves had bronzed upon the oak;
Said I, now cheerless days are done,
My pilgrimage shall be begun.

*Cecil Lay's footstone
at Aldringham*

19

To Suffolk

When swallows hawked in golden air,
And flowers were blooming everywhere,
When shores were gay with bathers bright,
And glow-worms greenly shone at night,
When hay was mown, and cuckoos flown,
And summer held her golden throne;
When cherries shone amidst their green,
And apples on the boughs were seen;
Said I, the time has come to start!
This home and I will shortly part.

When martlets left the cobwebbed eaves,
And russet corn was bound in sheaves,
When sunflowers bent their aureoled heads,
And spiders spun their migrant threads;
When skies were poems ready writ,
And morning mists were infinite;
When berries dazed the insect throng,
And leaves fell through the robin's song;
Said I, the season passeth by,
My luck upon the road I'll try.

When winds were wild, and roofs untiled,
And coloured leaves in corners piled;
When bat and dormouse went to sleep,
And bough and sky did frequent weep;
When nuts were plucked, and medlars sucked;
And pheasants shot, and furrows mucked;
When suns were dim and days were brief,
And winds re-howled their ardent grief;
Said I, the road now calleth me,
A pilgrim once again I'll be.

When pool and stream were frozen hard,
And cattle stayed within the yard;
When elms were red, and ash-trees black,
And sparrows robbed the farmer's stack;
When tilth and fallow changed to stone,
And hoodies fought around a bone;
When hands were numb and minds depressed,
When snow the naked trees had dressed;
Said I, I will away from here
In this hard season of the year.

Yet here I stay and years go by,
And Suffolk knows the reason why.

One Night of Love in Ipswich

If you think you are about to read a tale of raunchy eroticism in Ipswich, I'm sorry ole partner, you int!

The year is 1934. The film "One Night of Love" starring Grace Moore and featuring an Oscar winning score by Louis Silver is showing at the Picture Palace in the Suffolk county town.

It was the first holiday a small lad remembered. He was going with his family from the Waveney Valley to stay with grandparents in Ipswich. His first long journey from Beccles to Ipswich on a steam train. Mum had often taken him as a toddler to watch the trains at the station and now he was to experience the thrill of going "right up the line" to Ipswich.

He had been chance-time to Lowestoft and the seaside on the train. This journey took less than twenty minutes. But on the trip to Ipswich they would be in a railway carriage for one whole hour. Hard for his "little ole mind" to comprehend at first, until it was explained it was as long as the grandfather clock at home took between striking the hour. Time was hard to measure. The five minutes when he was told to "keep you quiet" when the news was read on the wireless seemed an eternity. Yet the excitement of the train journey made an hour fly past.

His Mother had told him about the railway line and all the different people who worked on it. Before she married his Dad, she had been the manageress of the Refreshment Rooms at the Railway Station. It excited him when they arrived to board their carriage to see that everyone new her and was pleased to see her. "How are yer goin' on Titch?" they said and smiled as they helped with the luggage. It was an odd way to greet her, he thought, but she seemed quite at ease with the title.

It was during this holiday that for the first time in his life his Mum and Dad left him when they went to see Grace Moore at the pictures. His Grandparents gave him such undivided attention that he was unconcerned when his parents departed for the film. He wished that "One Night of Love" took place every week!

They had a special tea that night. The fire in his holiday home seemed to glow much brighter. It was spring-time, but like many Suffolk springs a Black-thorn Winter made the air chilly.

Grandad attended to the fire very effectively. A blackened kettle with water near the boil stood on the hob. The plan was to always have red glowing coals at tea time for toast making. After it was taken from the cool pantry, butter was placed on the hearth near the fire to soften. "No need to make it too sorft for toast, then you git more," Grandad said, winking at young Billy.

With Grandma carefully watching, he was allowed to hold the extendable toasting fork over the fire. Skill was required by the old lady when she cut the bread for this fork. Too thin and it would flop and fall into the fire. Slices like a doorstep were unsatisfactory and indelicate. As he grew up the boy realised that most Suffolk households followed their own special ritual in the cutting of bread, before the dismal advent of the sliced loaf. Most families had a designated bread slicer who became skilled in the art. The need for every kitchen to have an adequate bread-board and a well sharpened knife, wielded by a deft operator, was essential. Even so accidents occured. A bandaged finger was more likely to be the result of a mishap at bread slicing than anything else.

The toasted bread was stored by the fire as each slice was completed. The butter was liberally applied, and allowed to soak into the toast. When enough was prepared the laden plate came to the table. An abundant coating of home-made blackcurrant, strawberry or bullace jam was added and the pile of toast soon disappeared. Fire toasted bread always had a flavour superior to that done under the grill. Modern electric toasters were one of the "things to come."

When the toast and jam was finished a further treat was in store. A special cake had been prepared for the holiday makers. Except at Christmas, the lad had never tasted such a cake. The spicing was different and marzipan ran through the middle. Lots of boys and girls today go out for a Happy Meal! Not one has a happier meal than this.

More treats were in store on this holiday. The lad went with Grandad up the yard to the "holy of holies", his shod. Here he discovered something that was to last all his life, the benefits and joys of a shod (shed)! Grandad called it his hideaway. "Everyone needs one!" he said. Although not so luxuriously furnished as the house it had a fascination about it no house ever had. There were two old seats taken from the back of a trolley-bus. The window on

The "holy of holies"

one wall was long and faced the sunshine of the south. There were a few plants in pots nearby, one with orange berries. "Don't you try and eat them," he was warned. At the end furthest from the door was another small window. Beneath it stood a small work bench, a vice and various tools and equipment. Standing by this bench were three or four damaged spades, forks and shovels plus an old muck crome. They belonged to neighbours and were there for repair. No charge was made for this service but vegetables or fruit came in return. Some of these carrots and potatoes were stored in hessian sacks in the shed. Set in a large wooden crate were the remainder of the last cooking apples. The sort that keep "until apples come agin." Some looked a bit clung. But Grandma said "good enough to make an apple dumplin' afore you go home."

Not everything in the shed was functional and useful. Not uncomfortably tidy, but it was orderly. The young lad sat on the trolley-bus seat time Grandad sharpened the kitchen knives with a special paste. He wore an apron for this made of green baize.

On the wall there was a large framed photograph of Grandad in younger days as a cricket umpire. He stood before the background of a pavilion with M.C.C. over the door. He loved to boast that he umpired for the M.C.C. After a pause, chuckle and a wink he let on that in his case it was Mistley Cricket Club!

The lad loved to be in the shod at any time, but after dusk it took on a greater enchantment. There was an oil stove and lamp giving warmth and a flickering light that was almost magical. Grandad said it "was comfortable enough to live in if you had to."

On a shopping trip into the town the family purchased the boy a pair of shining red rubber boots. They so thrilled him he wanted to wear them all the time.

The last job before bed, while Grandma made the cocoa, was to go up to the beloved shed to wash the boots spotless ready for the first walk in the morning. They always stood by the dying embers of the fire at night and were dry and warm to wear by morning.

Once abed the lad sat up suppin' his cocoa as Grandma read him a story about two little elves called 'Boogie' and 'Buzz' who lived in a potted plant. Later in the week he was certain that he saw them one evening in the biggest potted plant in the shed. But it might have been a trick of the shadows in the lamplight.

LAUGH WITH EPHRAIM

Nagging Plants

Ephraim and Willum were admiring some climbing plants all over the garden wall.

"Thass what I'd like on the front a my house," said Willum, "But I can't git any ter hang on my wall."

"You want ter git my missus to plant 'em, she'll drive anything up the wall!"

One of the Family

Everyone down at the village pub were of the same opinion and agreed when the landlord said, "I hardly doubt young Ken will be happy bein' a butcher." His father and his older brother Bob ran the butcher's shop in the high street. Young Ken was being schooled to join them.

His grandfather, Old Bob, now retired, always sat on a Suffolk chair in the corner of the shop. He loved to mardle alonga customers who were regulars and gave outsiders the benefit of the seel of the day. Often he would recall memories of his childhood and stories handed down from his great, great grandfather who had started the butchery business in the olden days. "Times have wholly changed since then," he said.

It was now the period between the two wars. The shop had a small slaughter house at the rear, a common custom in those days. A cousin who was a small-holder supplied them with pigs and poultry. Grandfather went with Ken's dad to buy fat bullocks at Wickham Market sale yard. The old man had a worthy reputation in the trade of having a "rare eye" for a good bullock. Sometimes his guidance was sort by local farmer friends and dealers when buying store cattle or young things. He soon spotted the ones likely to be good doers.

Long before his time to leave school Ken had to earn his pocket money as an errand boy. It was safe then for a twelve year old boy to push the shop trade bike, with its meat laden basket in the front, around the village.

He loved this part of the job, especially if calls had to be made at The Rectory, The Grove, Grange House or up at The Hall. For then a large twice weekly order might mean a penny tip. "Don't you hang about a lookin' for it," his

mother had told him. But he always whistled loud enough so everyone was aware: "The butcher's boy's a comin'."

The Grove soon became his favourite visit, for Gwen the "skivvy" collected the meat. She was a pretty girl, with golden hair, blue eyes, a saucy smile and dimples. Although he was a few years her junior with the wisdom of a country girl in these matters she realised he was a little in love with her. Albeit puppy love.

When he was 14 and just left school it was from Gwen he had his first kiss. It took place in the 'backus' under the mistletoe with a mince pie in his hand. She snuggled close to him and he dropped it on the kitchen floor. They both laughed. He went back up the drive humming a carol and wishing there was a Gwen at every house he called on. He loved mince pies but it was not them in his thoughts all that week.

Much as he liked being the errand boy there was a side of being the butcher's son he hated, the dealings in the slaughterhouse. It was his Mum who realised that Ken was too 'mure hearted' to work there. He was always quiet and pingled his food when they had been pig-killing or plucking poultry. "Bless yer heart I 'ont see em maake yah do it," she said.

The family had a conference with the bank manager and it was decided, when he was 18, they would set the lad up in a lock-up shop in a village about five miles away. The local butcher had retired some years before and with no family and sons to continue the business, the shop closed. Here was a splendid opportunity. Ken re-opened the business on his own and now employed his own errand boy. Meat and poultry were supplied direct and ready for sale from his father's business. Thus Ken was absolved from the horrors of a slaughterhouse.

His mother had a friend in the area looking for a lodger who readily agreed that she would be pleased to take Ken. It was very useful to have a butcher as a lodger. As the shop prospered Ken soon realised he had made the right decision. He had a pleasant, easy way with the ladies, was helpful in advice and in providing the meat required. The business was brisk, grew and his good name spread throughout the area. All this taking place without the dreadful squeals of pigs being slaughtered. Pork pies and brawn were much more in Ken's line.

He was able to extend his hobby and talent for painting rustic scenes. A disused slaughterhouse at the rear of Ken's shop was converted into a small gallery displaying his talent. It proved an interest to locals and visitors alike. You didn't find many places in Suffolk where you could buy a pound of sausages and a framed marshland scene.

His landlady proved very amenable. She and her husband, a local school teacher, often had parties and entertained. A great leg-puller, she made sausage rolls with grease proof paper in the middle or mince-pies filled with chutney. Such tricks were never played on visitors or on Ken but only among the family. An excuse was soon made to have a party. For fun, little card flags would be placed on the various plates

stacked high with pies, cakes and sandwiches. These flags would be inscribed with the initials: 'F.L.O.' - family lay off, for something expensive or in short supply. If an item had an unlimited amount and reserves available in the kitchen, the flag on top carried the message: 'M.I.K.' - more in kitchen.

For amusement, one plate would be placed with a few slices of rather dried up plain cake. These carried a flag signal. R.S.P. - rather stale, push. Ken, who was invited to join in the hilarity, realised that he had fallen on his feet not only with the shop but also his digs.

The young butcher went home at week-ends but arrived back at his landlady's on Sunday at tea-time. On a Monday morning it was his habit to take a bundle of white collars to be washed and starched at the village laundry. It was the accepted custom at the time to wear a shirt for a few days, possibly a week in cool weather. But a clean collar attached to the shirt by front and back studs was used each day. It was these six or seven collars Ken took away every Monday to the laundry. He had a few rather eccentric habits. One was to wrap the collars for transport in old newspaper. His landlady had told him to no avail this was "not hardly how". He ought to find something more suitable to put the collars in.

One Monday Ken marched into the laundry all smiles and joviality. He plonked the collars down on the counter. As the girl in the laundry unwrapped the newspaper she gasped in astonishment when a big pile of shrimp heads and tails fell out. Remembering what they had all had for Sunday tea, Ken cried out: "Its my damned landlady." When he arrived at his digs that evening his favourite tea was waiting and he was greeted with a welcome "You're one of the family now." And in future his collars were transported in a lidded card-board laundry box his landlady gave him.

The Heron's Band in 1998

It ought to have been a jolly time
For all the flocks of buds,
The days were getting longer
And Winter almost past.
Wren say to her mate the Heron,
"I've good cause to sing at last"
"Don't you start on that again",
Say Harnser melancholy,
"When I remember I can't sing
I near go orf my trolley"
"Sorry," say Wren, she really loved to sing
In Winter, Summer, Autumn
But especially when twas Spring.
She was full of the joys of the Season
And with such a zest for life
The last thing on her mind
Was to bring their friendship strife.
As she searched her tiny bird-brain
perched on a Hawthorn twig,

An inspired idea come to her
And she did a little ole jig.
Heron, say - "whas goin' on brown feathers?
You got some scheme in hand?"
"Yes; your problems can be solved.
Form the non-singing buds in a band"
Heron stood up all regal
As only a Harnser can.
"Thas a super idea you've given me
How about this for a plan?
We'll get rooks and crows on trombones
On the strings 'haps Magpies or Jay
We'll all clear orf down the marshes
to herald the break of day.
There we'll find ducks, geese or even
A Swan to give drums a clatter.
They can puddle their web feet up and down
The louder the din the better.
A Pheasant can play a clarinet

32

With a Partridge on the flute.
Thas better than being blown out
of the sky
By them humans on a shoot."
"But hold you hard," say Jenny ,
"You must play something grand"
"Don't worry," say ole Harnser,
"I'm goin' to conduct the band
Thanks Wren, you grant my wish
I'd ask you round for supper
But I doubt you'd fancy fish."

Suffolk's Secret Weapon

When the war came in 1939 life changed for everyone. Young and old, male and female, all had to cope with a different life. But it was not the disaster pessimists anticipated. On the contrary, for the first time a wholly lot of people had a new found and added purpose for living. Tragically, many over the next five years had to also make it a reason for dying.

Folks soon came to terms with the fact that they would all be involved with the war in various ways. All and sundry found the gainest way round their problems. To be a house-wife, mother and homemaker, seeking the best ways of feeding, clothing and keeping your family warm became a challenge rather than a drudge.

A small group who selfishly tried to look after themselves and engaged in black market activities found it didn't work in Suffolk. Soon a bonding of people occurred and networks developed seeing that mutual benefits arose. Class was still maintained and accepted but everyone happily mixed and joined the various war-time groups and organisations formed to contend with the emergencies.

Father's new purpose was to become an air raid warden and his black steel helmet found a place on the hat pegs in the hall. It was marked boldly with the initials ARP. 'Ere long, this rather shy and quiet man was promoted to Senior Warden in charge of the "Post" in the district where he lived and was proud to wear a white helmet showing his rank.

One of his most rewarding jobs began before the war. It was to fit all the small children in the area with gas masks. He became a welcome guest in many local homes that he might never have visited but for the war. Soon he was pleased to be greeted by most families in the street with "Mornin' or Arternune". His new found role of family protector delighted him.

A gas warning indicator was erected in our small terrace cottage front garden. Looking like a roofless bird-table the top was covered in special "scientific" paint. The theory was that the paint would change colour in the event of a gas attack. The chemistry master from a local grammar school was appointed official advisor to the ARP in the control and safety of everyone in the event of a gas attack. A massive responsibility compared to dealing with stink bomb attacks in his school chemistry laboratory. He took his job very seriously but luckily his control schemes were never put to the test.

To give warning of a gas attack Air Raid Wardens were provided with hand rattles of the type used at one time by boys on the farm to go 'bahd scarin' and by local football supporters. Father kept his on the umbrella stand when war began. As the years passed and the likelihood of a gas attack diminished it was placed in a cupboard. Children who were aware of its presence were warned not to play with it. When the war finally came to an end many a joyful youth or maiden swung those rattles around the streets with gusto.

Most towns and villages in Suffolk were victims of bomb or machine gun attack. Thank God gas masks and rattles were never required. A man living in the road who had been gassed in the trenches during the Great War warned everyone: "If Gerry drop them things that will be a rum ole do." Anyone who heard him years later, an old man, coughing and hawking from the mustard-gas filled lungs of his youth, realised what he meant.

The Air Raid Warden's post was manned at night by a warden on duty. In the event of an air raid or warning, the siren on the local police station roof sounded its mournful wail and all the wardens reported to the post. The siren continued for one minute and they were all expected to be out of the house and hurrying down the road to the post before it had finished. Their were three men and two ladies, all in blue

Suffolk's Secret Weapon

uniform of trousers and battle dress top. The ARP insignia was bright egg yolk yellow, the colour yolks were before factory farming.

The war made it acceptable for ladies to wear trousers, but for some reason or other they were always referred to as slacks. When turning out at night to brave a Suffolk Winter's north-easter they were essential. "I can wear Albert's coms in the cold weather under slacks," the ARP lady said, "but I'd look sorft if I put them on under a skirt."

The post became quite an important focal point on many wartime nights, for it was in a strategic area. Within a few hundred yards was a railway junction, a maltings and an iron foundry engaged in munitions manufacture. As the war progressed, army billets, depots and a cook house were established in the area.

The early years of the war saw the air raid post fulfil all its official duties. Additional to this, in a typical Suffolk way it became famous for bending bureaucratic rules. Anyone lonely or nervous during a wartime night was welcome to come and spend time at the post provided they did not interfere or disturb official duties. Some of these folks, often older or frail people, were able to help by answering the telephone or generally keeping an eye on things. They even helped in the important job of dishing out drinks or biscuits.

One of the drinks was special and eventually became famous. Father's cocoa was known as 'Suffolk's Secret Weapon.' The renown of it spread far beyond the district. The method of preparation was copied throughout the kingdom! At least as far as Bungay!

Fire-watchers on duty at the maltings, railway station and iron foundry strolled along for fortification. The local constable or "special" on his beat dropped by for refreshment. There were even occasions when the Police Superintendent and a local Army Colonel arrived to see if the cocoa merited the claims made. They agreed it did. Railway men on duty at the station at night strolled the few yards to ask "how yah gittin on bor". They were never known to refuse "a cuppa cocoa". The local doctor or midwife on call at night came to fortify themselves. An empty cocoa tin stood in the post and donations were left for the cocoa fund.

Now over fifty years after the use of "Suffolk's Secret Cocoa Weapon" its means of preparation can safely be disclosed. If Europe is to consider monetary union why should Suffolk not share its cocoa preparation methods? Having arrived at the number of cups required a large tea spoonful of cocoa was allowed for each. This was mixed to a smooth paste in milk with the "chill off" in a small pudding basin. Great care had to be taken to see their were no lumps. On the kitchen gas ring a large saucepan of half milk and half water was heated almost to boiling. To this was added the thick creamy cocoa paste. The whole was allowed to gently simmer for four minutes. All this time it was stirred with a wooden spoon and care was taken to see it did not boil furiously. When the exigencies of war time restrictions allowed, one teaspoon of rum or brandy was added per pint of cocoa. Owing to the uncertain and irregular supply of spirits this was mostly kept in reserve for the bitterest weather. Supplies of rum, however, improved for a time because one of the wardens had a niece who became very kind to some American air-men stationed in the area. Lease/lend took many forms of mutual benefit. During the early months of the war Father took the prepared cocoa to the air raid post in warmed thermos flasks. But it was soon decided cocoa making equipment using a double gas ring was needed on site. Whenever possible the Senior Warden would supervise its preparation. Try as they might nobody else's cocoa was quite the same. Small wonder it became known as "Suffolk's Secret Weapon."

During the commemorative celebrations that took place in 1995 to mark fifty years since the end of the war, memories of the Senior Warden's cocoa were revived in his part of Suffolk.

The Wren and Heron Go on an Outin'

A little Jenny Wren, wi' an ole Heron
Flew out on an outin' one day.
Did you know buds allust have a trip out
Afore nestin' time git under way?
Now they had to be up pretty arly
Although not quite with the lark.
Luckily buds don't muck the clock about
They just go orf to perk when thas dark.

Addressin' remarks to the Heron
Say the Wren, in a bickitty way,
"Don't you miss not joining in bud-song?
My family all sing through the day."
Well! The poor ole Harnser looked down-cast
And even a little more grey.
They'd just flown over an orchard
And he dint really know what to say!

"You're brown, small and round wi' your tail up
And creep round a tree like a mouse.
Your nest, minute, warm and cosy
Would never do me for a house
I have to live high in the tree tops
On a bed like nails made of sticks.
Some reckon my legs dangle through it
But that just int one of my tricks.

So when, at the sunrise dawn chorus,
You sing full blast with each breath
In our wind blown house in the branches
We're all hanging on for grim death.
But life has got compensations
And for me I've only one wish:
For a marsh and tall reeds to hide in
And a pond thas stocked full of fish".

The Confederate

Teddy would never have given himself the title of "the confederate". But that was how his best pal and assumed boss referred to him. They were in league together for many years from the early 1930's until after the second world war. They had known each other long before but it was during this time that they became partners and conspirators in numerous escapades. Not wicked designs I must hasten to add, but for their own or their families mutual benefit. Thus the term confederate was apt.

Maybe it was so in most of Great Britain but certainly in East Anglia at the time it was the custom that the title given to people varied according to their gender, rank or class. Teddy was meticulous in adhering to it. But his dark watery eyes, a relic from an attack of Bell's Palsy, often twinkled as he spoke. He played a game which his position demanded and his survival required. Working for a local auctioneer and estate agent, his job was to act as caretaker and keeper come handy man at their sale-yard. Here he would spend most of the working week. Three brothers owned the business but he had little direct contact with them. It was to the chief clerk that he owed and shew allegiance.

Teddy called the chief clerk "Sir" to his face but when talking about him to others, whether fellow workers or sale yard clients, he referred to him as CWJ. When he deemed it necessary to obtain confirmation to proceed with some action connected with his work, assuming a quasi reverence he would utter, "I think tha's best to ask CWJ." Maybe in turn CWJ would prudently consult one of the auctioneers on an important matter, for he was the link in a hierarchical chain of command.

The Sale Yard

The sale yard work followed a natural flow. Sale day was on alternate Fridays and Teddy acted as one of five drovers for the cattle, pigs and calves arriving at the market. Saturday mornings were spent tidying up the office and sheds. Monday and Tuesday he removed the muck and straw from the pigpens. He carried it on a wooden crudbarra to a muck-heap on a large allotment garden adjoining the sale yard. Teddy and a relative, a local head postman, cultivated this parcel of land. Postmen are good gardeners as they usually have some free time most days. Also their early start in the mornings did not allow them to have late night social activities. It was a very advantageous position for their vegetable garden to be near such a regular supply of free pig-muck.

Thursday was spent in cleaning and washing bullock and calf pens and scrubbing the sale ring and weigh-bridge. And so back to Friday again.

Now had there been a sale at his yard every Friday, Teddy's routine would have been a very dull one week in week out. Fortunately for him and CJW, the firm they worked for had a rival who had a livestock market at the other end of the town on the next Friday. Then Teddy and CWJ plus a couple more staff were loaned to the rival at the second sale yard for their busy day.

There was a reciprocal agreement whereby some of their chaps came to help Teddy and CWJ. An outstanding arrangement. Can you imagine Tesco's staff helping Safeway when things get hectic? But in a typical Suffolk manner the system worked to the mutual benefit of both firms. They were able to manage most days on a minimum staff requirement. But when needed, each secured the service of skilled staff experienced in the rigours of a busy livestock mart. There was not enough demand for two weekly sales. Yet neither wanted to put the other out of business. Would such an attitude prevail today?

CWJ and Teddy reported to their temporary boss on his sale day. They were given similar

... his boots always shone

jobs to their usual ones and the set up was even more congenial because Teddy's brother-in-law was caretaker at the other sale yard.

There was some conflict early on which CWJ soon put right. His temporary governor referred to him as Johnson without the prefix Mr that his real boss always used. Quietly looking him full in the eyes CWJ remarked: "My proper boss always calls me Mr Johnson, if you wish me to work for you please do the same." There was a long pause, the two looking each other steadily in the eyes before they walked away. But from then on CWJ was always Mr Johnson.

On sale days, wherever the venue, Teddy and CJW dressed for the occasion. Not to the extent of wearing Sunday best but their work clothes were always clean on for sale day. Teddy had a spotless Khaki drover's coat and a clean red and white neckerchief and his boots always shone. They glistened at the start of the day even if cattle and pig muck had taken the shine from them by evening. He always wore a smarter and newer cloth cap than his normal workaday one. CWJ would never have gone "into the office" as he called it, shabbily dressed. But on sale days his boots and buskins shone brightly and he wore his best trilby. Their dress, though different, was very important to them both.

CWJ and his confederate had a genuine arrangement whereby each gained from the expertise and time they could give helping each other. Any letters, paperwork filling in of club forms were done by CWJ. The term pen-pusher was sometimes used in a derogatory way towards office workers by those engaged in manual work. But Teddy never used such a term about his accomplice in the way some might have done. He was grateful to CWJ for shopping in the town centre for him where he got his groceries and butcher's meat. This was beneficial as Teddy and his wife grew older. They had no children.

Quite a procedure was entailed in the purchase of butchers meat. CWJ would observe where the top quality cattle had gone from the livestock market and made sure the weekend joint came from one of these. The butchers and dealers had a tremendous respect for him. Described as "honest as the day is long," sale-yard customers would sign blank cheques for him to complete at the end of the day when their bill had been reckoned. It saved busy farmers, dealers and butchers wasting time.

Mondays Teddy would arrive bearing vegetables from the sale yard allotment and a debate would ensue concerning the quality and flavour of the weekend joint.

Teddy never forgot CWJ's two children at Christmas when an envelope containing a bright new sixpenny piece was given to go in their stocking. A similar gift also came with their birthday cards.

But the two boys were equally grateful for something else Teddy brought to their household every week. Saffron Buns at a halfpenny each! Dusty was a small local baker whose bread and buns were unsurpassed by any in the parish. His bakehouse was near to Teddy's abode. On his way back to the sale yard after his midday dinner break he made a slight detour, called at the bakery and loaded his bike with two hessian carrier bags filled with bread and buns, destined for CWJ's household. Tea time was then anticipated with relish.

CWJ's wife loved what Dusty described as his rasped loaf. These were over baked in the oven before removal, thus covered by a darkened, scorched crust. This was then rasped or scraped by a unique home-made tool the baker kept specifically for the purpose. He made it by tacking metal crown beer bottle tops arse uppards on to a square of a quarter inch thick wood measuring about eight by eight inches. The loaf was whacked by the side of the tool to loosen the cindery crust then roughly rasped removing the scorched parts. When finished although the bread looked a bit peeled it had an exquisite nutty flavour. A farm buttered slice from a freshly baked, rasped loaf, was better than a slice of cake. But the boys thought the halfpenny saffron buns even better.

On Good Friday, Dusty made a special bake of Hot Cross Buns. Similar in style but with a pastry cross on top, locals queued on Good Friday morning and collected them for breakfast. All the local bakers had similar bakes of Hot Cross Buns, but only on Good Friday - not from Boxing day until Easter. The joy of a Hot Cross Bun for breakfast on Good Friday was much greater then.

Teddy's arrival with the bread and buns was followed by the same routine. He was able to take a short cut to CWJ's cottage by pushing his laden bike along two back lanes. Leaning the bike against the garden wall he then came up the yard to the back door with the bread. Although his arrival was anticipated and he entered the house on each visit he always tapped on the back door. "Come in Mr. Dray" CWJ's wife would call. She and her sister-in-law who lived in the cottage always gave Teddy the title of Mr. Dray. It would have been incorrect to have been more familiar. "Thank

You Ma'am" he said to Mrs. Johnson as she opened the back door. Miss Johnson would be hovering in readiness to enquire if Teddy would like a coffee. This he gratefully accepted with the words "Thank You Ma'am - I mean Miss." Miss being the title he thought correctly assigned to a single lady, no matter her age. The ladies were greatly amused by this, so amused they fed him the questions like a comedian's straight man.

Teddy then always pulled his coat off. "So I get the benefit when I go ma'am" he confided.

When Miss Johnson asked him during the Winter if he wanted a seat nearer the fire he replied, "No thank you Miss. If I get too comfortable and warm I 'ont want to go. Mustn't be an old fire spaniel." He always supped his coffee at the start with the teaspoon. The drink was piping hot, well sweetened and milky. He drew it into his mouth noisily through his lips. The first two swallows always followed by a satisfied "Aah." When the usual offer of a slice of cake or biscuit was made Teddy's reply was, "I doubt I better not, the Missus 'ont like it if I spoil m'tea." But an exception to this was made during the week before Christmas when he accepted the offer of a mince pie and a drop of rum in his coffee. After about 10 minutes, Teddy rose with the words, "Best be gettin' on." He left, saying as he donned his cap on going into the back yard, "Fare ye well ma'am, Fare ye well miss."

Confederacy yielded many chuckles and simple benefits for Teddy, CWJ and their families.

LAUGH WITH EPHRAIM

Second Opinion

Ephraim's missus hadn't been feeling too well so she went to see the doctor. On her return Ephraim asked her how she got on.

"He say wot I need is a long holiday by the sea. Where du yu think I orter go?"

"To see another doctor I should think," replied Ephraim.

Bullace and Pear Jam

Approximate yeild: 10 lbs.

Ingredients

3 lbs pears, peeled and finely diced
3 lbs bullaces (or damsons)
1 pint water
1 teaspoone citric acid
6 lbs sugar

Method

Place the fruit in separate saucepans, each with half pint of water. Add the citric acid to the pears. Simmer both fruits until tender. Sieve the stones from the bullaces then add the purée to the pears.

Add the sugar, stir well until dissolved, then boil the mixture rapidly until setting point is reached, removing any scum from the surface as it appears. Pour into warmed jars, cover with waxed circles and cellophane covers.

The Wren and Heron on a Fine Day

Little Jenny Wren and the ole Harnser
Come a bright and fine Autumn day
Stood on the hoss knoll in the morning
Looking round, to weigh up and survey.
"Did you ever know such weather?" say Wren
And for once trying to be so polite
The day afore she'd snapped at the grey bard
Upset him, and he'd had such a bad night.

For just like us humans and mortals
Poor birds can have a bad day
And the Wrens had got so fed up
'Cos that had rained and rained in a way
That no living Wren could remember.
No matter how long they thought back
Night arter night they all huddled
Under the lee of a chimney stack.

Five blarmed nests wi' been washed from,
Thas a wonder we didn't all drown.
That make you want to leave country
Fly orf and go and live in the Town.
"That rain there too" said ole Harnser
"But this morning, as you're bein' so nice
Listen to wise words that I utter,
And I'll give you some real good advice.

Water for me int much problem
Chance time, that spreed out the fish,
And I have to look further and harder
When I search for my supper-time dish
But don't fret about what you 'ont alter
The weather will come as it will
We all must accept the elements
If you worry: that will make you ill.

Enjoy the sun, time we got it.
And the friendship that we all share
The berries will soon be a ripening
With more 'an enough to spare
I know that this here wet weather
For many that surely 'ont suit
But you look along all them hedgerows
And thank God for the harvest of fruit".

The Confederates in Wartime

The strength of the confederacy grew with the years. Never did either look to gain from their friendship, each used his position to benefit the others or their mutual gain. Both loyal to their employer, their loyalty to each other was even greater. But such was the trust the auctioneers had in them, their various extra activities were never questioned.

During the year before the second world war, as a result of a big clear up at the sale yard and at land nearby a "gret ole" pile of rubbish accumulated. CWJ realised this could be made use of as Guy Fawkes night got near. Once the plan was hatched word soon got around to the sale yard regulars. Contributions of old wood, cardboard and similar combustible material arrived. By the time November the fifth arrived there was, what Teddy described as the "masterest gret heap of stuff I ever did see."

And so thanks to the confederates one of the most exciting Guy Fawkes celebrations the families ever remembered took place. Teddy was master of the bonfire, and with dry straw starting it, an enormous blaze was soon licking into the sky.

Several family and friends pooled their resources and a large box of fireworks was jointly purchased. The prize one of the evening, a Roman Candle, contributed by one guest that had cost him half a crown. It caused much comment because quite a reasonable firework was purchased for one penny. There were also whizz-bang aeroplanes that flew up and clattered along the corrugated iron roof of the pig pens. A successful and memorable evening. But soon war was to be declared and the fireworks seen in Suffolk were to be of a more sinister kind.

CWJ about this time was able to use his influence in soothing a turbulent episode that suddenly blew up one sale day between Teddy and the principal auctioneer who was an irascible character blowing hot and cold very quickly. The chief drover was absent so Teddy was called upon to display the cattle in the sale yard ring.

He hated this job, preferring the task of penning the cattle or driving them into the ring. But his work that day placed him in full view of his boss plus many farmers and dealers. It was a busy day with many beasts passing through the sale ring. Unfortunately Teddy was not getting them away as quickly as he wanted when "knocked down" by the auctioneer. There were several quiet requests to speed up but suddenly he was loudly told "Hurry up Dray, we don't want to be here all night."

This was too much even for his placid temperament. He was tired, but more than anything he felt ridiculed in front of all the people he saw each week. Without further ado,

he paused, looked up at the auctioneer seated on his rostrum above the ring, "You better git someone else to do your work, sir - if I 'int good enow." And he walked from the ring, swapping jobs with a young drover.

When the day finished, Teddy, somewhat worried and subdued, walked into the office to collect his £1 wage for the days work. CWJ was at the counter paying out; their boss was in the background. But in the meantime CWJ had spoken a few consiliatory words with him. As Teddy walked down the steps out of the office he paused looking towards the auctioneer who had shouted at him earlier. A slight grin came on both their faces. Then the boss exclaimed, "Looks as if there will be a lot of tidying up for you on Monday." It was his way of saying sorry for the outburst. Teddy's job was secure and never again was he humiliated

When the war came the partnership took on great significance. CWJ, aided by Teddy, turned his small back garden into a mini-farmyard. An exaggeration of their achievement maybe but it was remarkable what they were able to do. Pre-war the back garden was typical of a terraced cottage in a small Suffolk market town in the Waveney Valley.

However it did have one or two aspects which gave it a grandeur beyond the cottage status. A large bay tree against one wall provided a flavour for rice puddings and stews, plus sanctuary for house sparrows and the odd robin or wren. There was a linty shod. The privvy faced west into the setting sun and joining it a coal shod. There was a rockery and a small patch of grass plus a flower bed with pinks and a few other plants which varied from year to year. But the garden was made splendid by a cob-nut tree. Of great age it had a sizeable trunk and four main branches. Although trimmed so as not to encroach across the neighbour's fence it was very climbable and able to support a small swing. The two trees survived the war time changes but otherwise the garden was transformed. Soon it ceased to be called a garden but the back yard.

CWJ and Teddy decided they would keep hens for eggs and fatten poultry and rabbits. It was soon agreed, "Best git on with it afore the nights pull in." A small henus was recovered from the sale yard where it had lain unsold and getting more dilapidated every month. Large enough to take six hens, it had a war time revival conjured by Teddy when he had a spare moment. He carefully sorted out odd bits and pieces that in former days might have gone on the bonfire and these were used to make the "ole henus" a satisfactory abode. The sections of the house were transported on a builder's flat barrow and erected in CWJ's back yard one weekend in the first month of the war. A covered wire netting run adjoined the house so the "ole hens could scrap about." Fattening coops were provided to house around twenty cockerels finishing for the table. Teddy reared the birds in their early stages acquiring them from a friendly farmer supplier. Three large rabbit hutches added to the livestock housing. Two breeding Flemish Giant does provided offspring destined for rabbit pies or stews. A rabbit breeding expert lived in the vicinity and was more than happy to loan his prize Belgian Hare buck for official duties. No payment was made for this "service" but the buck's owner had the pick of the litter for his own consumption. This particular cross at the time was noted for its hybrid vigour.

CWJ's family soon realised which members of the farmyard they could make into semi-pets without eventual heartache. The breeding does and the ole hins came into this category. Anyone who has ever kept hens will be able to tell you that after a time they each develop an individual character. But there is invariably one in a group that stands out wings and feathers before the others. Such a one in this collection was Hetty. A Rhode Island Red with a massive comb and wattle that would not have disgraced a cockerel. But there was no other masculine traits about this wily old bird, except perhaps the fact she was number one in the pecking order. Whenever possible the ole hens were let out of their run to the freedom of the garden - or yard to give it the changed war-time name.

Hetty found that to be near the back door was a useful place for extra scraps. Carrot peelings, Brussels sprout trimmings or cabbage waste being very popular. There were other advantages for hens near the back door, warmth and music. They soon discovered that the bricks, heated by sun from outside, and the household heating inside raised the winter air temperature a few degrees.

The bay tree near the back door provided a sheltered scratching area that only froze hard in the coldest weather. But Hetty and three more at the top of the hen hierarchy found if they perched on the window sill near the back door they could listen to the wireless. This was placed at a vantage point so that when the man came to change the accumulator all he had to do was raise the sash window. Hetty spent much of her time there, winter or summer. She left to lay the odd egg but many hours were spent listening to music. Melodic strings were her favourite. On a warm summer evening when "henus shut up" was late, Albert Sandler and the Palm Court orchestra were a must. She would tolerate Big Bands or Worker's Playtime or even hymn singing, but when the news came on Hetty was away concerned with her henly business. Over a cup of tea or coffee the Confederates and family spent many an amusing moment discussing the exploits of Hetty and her clan. But as Teddy said, "Don't matter what they do so long as they keep a laying."

The three children in the household were co-opted as aids in the rabbit production venture. CWJ supervised the feeding while the boys were used to collect the rabbit food. There were two main sources for this. In autumn and winter the local greengrocers were the main source of supply. The boys went round to their shops asking for carrots and celery tops, plus the trimmed outer leaves of cabbages and cauliflower. Cheap swedes or turnips that were not of best cooking quality but suitable to feed rabbits were available. These would be invaluable in a hard winter like 1943 when any green fodder was scarce.

In the late spring and summer months the boys set out along the hedgerow in search of sow-thistle and hog-weed. This was picked into hessian bags and transported resting on the cross-bar of their bikes as they pushed them home. Care was taken by CWJ to wilt this before feeding. Now and again Teddy would arrive from the sale yard with a couple of bags of hay. A truss or two were kept at the sale yard gifted by a local farmer in return for some favour by the confederates.

The run up to Christmas was the main time for fattening poultry. Chicken was a luxury in the majority of households in those days. Conveyor belt production and processing did not arrive until after the war. The fattening coops were arranged along the back yard boundary fence and faced east towards the hen run. That way the birds got the benefit of early sunshine and the soothing sight of their more fortunate sisters scratching in the back yard. The Cockerels also seemed to enjoy the "ole hens" prateing. Happy birds eat better and put on weight quickly. Alas they did not have the joy of listening to Albert Sandler and his Palm Court orchestra as Hetty and her chums did.

The cockerels were fed a wet mash twice daily, early in the morning and a few minutes before dusk. It was thought that a full crop at bed time was another aid to weight gain. Barley meal was obtained from a local farmer, any household scraps like old bread and potatoes were added, plus Balancer meal obtained from the local corn chandler. Sometimes, if the birds looked a bit off colour, a supplement known as "Poultry Spice" was used. It smelt of aniseed, and was put in the mash which was mixed with water to a damp crumbly consistency. This dropped easily from the large mixing spoon into the bird's trough placed outside, along the front of their coop. They stuck their heads through the railed front to feed. Standing on a slatted floor about waist high their droppings fell to the ground below. These were collected every week and taken as a gift to any one of three neighbours in the road, who were the local tomato growers. The droppings were allowed to weather and loose the ammonia. They were stored dry and as spring came and tomato plants appeared in the green houses a chicken muck cocktail was used to feed them. Propriety feeds were not available in wartime. There were various methods used in preparing this mixture, each individual had his own preferred way. But the basic idea was to dissolve the chicken muck in a butt of rain water. A sludge sank to the bottom and this was stirred periodically. The tomato feed was made by diluting the mixture from the butt in more water. It was in this respect that the gardeners real skill was apparent. As the tomato plants grew and eventually produced flowers and fruit the feed increased in strength and volume.

The supply of free manure to neighbouring tomato producers was a tactful move by the confederates. The growers repaid in kind.

Tomatoes were a very beneficial edition to a restricted war time diet. At the time the government was making a heating fuel allowance to commercial growers producing tomatoes. It was known that extra tomatoes would make up for the lack of citrus fruits. But it paid the confederates even further to keep on the right side of their neighbours. The early morning chorus from fattening cocks could be quite disturbing. Although this took place chiefly in the winter, when the cocks crew quite late at sunrise, they did however make a considerable dullor. It was not often the confederates could spare a chicken for neighbours but now and again when eggs were plentiful around Easter-tide they had a few. Possibly a rabbit might be given to the tomato growers at least once in the year.

The rabbit muck was not used as local manure. As each batch went, Teddy and the boys cleaned the hutch and the straw and droppings were carted away on his barrow for the allotment muck heap at the sale yard.

The confederates also liased in various exploits with two or three friendly farmers or small holders who were regular clients at the sale yard. Such was the regard they were held in it was not surprising little favours came their way. CWJ would sometimes help them with a bit of paperwork. They also knew that Teddy would keep a weather eye on any stock, poultry or produce put up for sale. Because of their years of experience it was often useful to take their advice on what sort of price stuff might make. They also advised if a "reserve" ought to be placed on a commodity and if so at what level.

And so the Confederates continued through the war. When the Victory celebrations came, together they collected and displayed flags and bunting unearthed from chests and trunks from a big cupboard under the stairs. Eventually, as the hens declined with age they were not replaced. The breeding does were sold. The henus and coops were removed and sold. Teddy, now quite an elderly man, helped CWJ set rose bushes where the henus had been. One of the most popular being the aptly named Peace. On the other side, where the fattening coops had been, heavy cropping rows of runner beans were grown each year.

Teddy was replaced at the sale yard by a younger man but he was always a welcome caller. As he grew frailer his visits for coffee became less frequent and finally ceased. But CWJ continued to visit him and his wife until he died. Then he visited his widow, taking her small gifts and always a fowl at Christmas. CWJ, now well into his nineties in an old peoples' home in the town, would look into the office now and again to keep an eye on things. But his sale yard visits had ceased. He enjoyed nearly five years in his sheltered abode. The week before he died, realising his time was near he told his son, "Make sure you don't have my funeral on a Friday. That will make it difficult for them coming from the office on a sale day." Loyal to the end.

Autumn in Suffolk

The martins and the swallows they have left us,
School year begins, first day, try not to fuss,
Squirrels gather in their winter store,
As lacey cobwebs glisten joining hip to haw,
Fishermen pull in their nets as seagulls dip and soar,
Holidaymakers refreshed, have left our Eastern shore,
Like nature, life in Suffolk some may say,
Is richest, fullest, most serene upon an Autumn day.

Jean Kinge

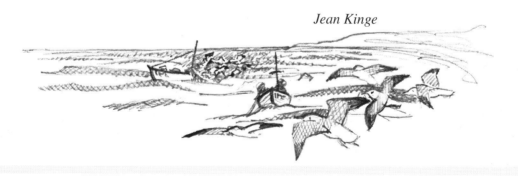

The Evacuee

Melvin was six years old when he came with his parents and younger brother on their regular annual Summer holiday to Suffolk. Even a child of his tender years was able to absorb the excitement that his Dad was feeling when they boarded the train at Liverpool Street Station. Dad loaded the large amount of holiday baggage onto the carriage racks with complete abandon. By the time the train had steamed through the tunnel at Ipswich he chuckled and remarked to Melvin's Mum that he felt "ten years younger."

The lad was confused when his Mum said the train was fast to Ipswich but slow for the rest of the journey. It seemed to go just as quick to him as they rattled across the Suffolk countryside. But he noticed fewer houses, factories and smoky chimneys as he looked out on to the now gently rolling landscape from his corner seat by the window. Harvest was in progress and once they passed a field with a binder cutting the wheat, men standing the "shoofs" into "shocks" and boys with sticks hurtling across the field. Melvin thought it was a funny game for lads to play. But what fun for the men with all that straw.

Later he was to learn from his holiday cousins about chasing rabbits in the harvest field. Now and again he was excited to see a sailing boat. Cattle grazed lazily in the summer heat on low lying water meadows. Some meadows were blotched by the yellow of buttercups. Melvin caught sight of a big grey bird flopping across marshland reeds. In awe he gripped Dad and pointed at the bird. "It's an ole harnser," said his Father. "Oh dear, don't teach the boy them words," said Mum, "the proper name is Heron."

At the now more frequent stops several passengers left the train. Small groups of family and friends waited to greet them eagerly. In those days few folk took holidays unless staying with relatives. The child was fascinated by the sound made by the porters on the platforms crying out the station names. "Weaster-Feld!" - "Wikka-Mar!" - "Saaks-mundham!" - "Haalesa!"

There was a resonant sing-song quality in their voice so different from the London suburban sound heard at their Surrey home. The train left Halesworth and soon they passed slowly over a level crossing. Suddenly Mum gripped her husband's shoulder and pointed to a long column of Army trucks and lorries that stretched up a slight incline in the narrow country road and out of sight. Some towed anti-aircraft guns and another a mobile searchlight. They were a sinister omen of the events his long awaited holiday would bring to all concerned.

Eventually they reached their destination. Although only a small market town the station was the most important on the Lowestoft - Ipswich line. Being a junction for the division of the train, half went to Lowestoft and the other carriages to Great Yarmouth. A guard walked along the corridor crying, "Yarmouth in front, Lowestoft in the rear!" A few bemused passengers hurriedly changed seats. Then the guard called "Change for all Waveney Valley passengers!" For it was from this station that the "Crab and Winkle" train chugged across the marshes of the valley to Bungay, Harleston and Tivetshall.

Uncle Jack shepherded them to his nearby home in a trice. Aunt Olive greeted them with fond hugs and a cold ham and salad tea. "I thought it best we had something cold," she said, "It's so hot and the train might have been late."

Their holiday plans today would seem tame, but being only a few miles from Lowestoft and Great Yarmouth, days on the beach were easily arranged. Donkey rides and trips on the famous electric boats at Kensington Gardens were a

joy. A charabanc ride to Southwold and Dunwich, where the coastal serenity appealed more to the grown ups, was a regular. But the youngsters amused themselves as all children can with the beach, sea, buckets and spades.

One holiday feature, even in the years before Melvin was born, was the family's pilgrimage to the Lock House Pub on the river. Melvin had been told about the delicious scones, cream and home-made strawberry jam that awaited them at the Lock House. He also heard his Uncle say that the motor boat would cost half a crown an hour. He was going to be allowed to steer the boat part of the way taking turns with his cousins.

On the Friday, in the first holiday week, his Dad and the two cousins strolled down to see the "Captain" at the riverside and to book the boat for the following Saturday. The high spot of the Suffolk sojourn was kept to the end. Alas it was not to be. Dad was surprised and bothered to find the Captain's riverside shed holding the tackle, oars and fuel for boat hire securely locked. What was also more startling was on this balmy early September morning, the Captain was not busy as usual at his small riverside quay. Concerned, they walked back to his dwelling a few yards up the loke that led to the river. The Captain greeted his Dad and the family as he climbed down a tall pair of steps from which he was fixing black-out material across a skylight on the hall landing. "Things don't look too good, we shall soon be at war again Claud," he said to Dad. The boys found it hard to comprehend the meaning of it all. But they sensed the anxiety in the grown ups' voices.

However, although the impact of the terrible disaster that had threatened for months was soon to become a reality — for the boys at that moment it had ruined a river trip and creamed scones with strawberry jam. Everyone heard the wireless speech from Neville Chamberlain saying War had been declared. The children were all given a threepenny Joey for keeping quiet. After an anxious and hurried discussion the lad was told that he was to stay much longer on holiday in Suffolk. Aunt Olive and his mum told him it would be best if he remained behind and went to school with his cousins. Otherwise, they tried to explain, that if he went home his own school was to be moved somewhere else. Much better to stay with his Uncle and family that he knew. But the lad had only one concern. All his toys were left in Surrey.

The early Autumn was mellow. It was fun playing marbles or Cowboys and Indians with his cousins and friends in the back lane. He struck up a special friendship with a boy called Billy Orchard from London who had also come to stay with an aunt. Together they explored the back lane and watched the sparks fly as the welders worked at the engineering workshop nearby. Little did he realise that eventually he was to make a good career in engineering as a pattern maker.

Soon his cousin's harvest holiday was over and his new school teachers did their best to make him welcome. Next to the school was a Drill Hall with Territorial soldiers and their equipment. They were soon to leave for France. No one thought it strange a military unit was so near a school. The lad was also surprised to see cattle on the hoof driven around to the sale yard in the vicinity.

Early in the school term the annual Michaelmas Hoss Sale took place. On his Uncle's advice they took a long detour in order to avoid the unbroken horses which were driven along the street where they normally walked to school. Diddy-coys ran ponies and cobs for sale outside a pub nearby where they gathered and set up deals. The trade was brisk in horse flesh and liquor. Arguments and robustious behaviour was common, the children were well advised to steer clear.

Ironically the early air raids of the war were mostly on the East Coast. While Melvin's family at home were undisturbed the lad soon found himself sitting with his cousins, Aunt and Great Aunt on the stairs, thought to be the safest place in the house. Melvin did not mind this too much but he was fearful of enforced trips to the privy in the back yard. This was worst when the first bitter Suffolk winter of the war came. Chilled to the bone he sat outside watching the searchlights moving through the sky.

Bath night was a big event for the crowded family. They all took it in turns to soak in a tin bath on the kitchen floor. A fire was lit in the corner beneath a copper to heat the water. It seemed warm and cosy at first but when someone opened the back door for an outside mission, the icy blast on a warm wet back took your breath away.

But Melvin's stay in Suffolk had its lighter moments. As long as he managed not to be pecked he quite enjoyed feeding his Uncle's chickens and collecting the eggs. The local milkman came with a horse and cart and ladled the milk into jugs. To everyone's amusement he told the family that at his home in Croydon their milk wasn't from cows but came from a factory, in bottles! As the first war time Christmas approached the maggot infested pheasants hanging in an out house caused a minor family dispute concerning their suitability to eat.

Church was a routine Sunday event. His older cousins took part in a Nativity play and his Uncle sang Good King Wenceslas. It was all different but fun.

They were all taken to see one film at the local cinema during his nine months in Suffolk. Called "Sixty Glorious Years", it was an historical drama about Queen Victoria, with 34 year old former ballerina Anna Neagle in the title role, Anton Walbrook as Prince Albert and C. Aubrey Smith as the Duke of Wellington. His Aunt and Uncle felt it was a suitable and patriotic film for them all to see and even the Great Aunts went.

Then suddenly during the early Summer of 1940 his mother arrived on the train from London. She was aware of the East coast raids and the talk of invasion. Maybe young Melvin would be safer in Croydon. So the lad went home and back to his old school. Before long the Battle of Britain started and as he says nearly sixty years later he had gone from the fat into the fire. But that's another story.

Three Firsts at Harvest Time

First had cold tea, at harvest time
Thought I! You 'ont like this.
It wetted my whistle wholly well,
Slaked my thirst, 'twas bliss.
Was only a boy, on boy's work,
About four years and ten.
Wanted to try and be grown up,
I was workin' wi' the men.
Thas the drink, when yah dry
Kept cool in a pulk and shade.
Always seemed to do the job
Better 'an fizzy-pop lemonade.

First had a pint at harvest time.
When we cycled home one night.
Pitched and loaded wheaat that day
and I'd done it quite alright.
You've earned a pinta beer boy,
No one'll tell your Dad

I'm a real man now, I thought
And I was wholly glad.
It came in a pot, looking so big
With a frawthy hid so white.
I downed it quick, like the men
Lawk! it made me tight.

First had a kiss at harvest time
As the sunset redded the sky.
Walk down the loke wi' me she said
Got something you'll love to try.
The fields were gold, her eyes were blue,
Her skin was as a peach.
Trembling, by the stile we stopped
For her lips I did beseech.
Warm and soft to me she was
Those lips they came to mine.
I held her close, she held me too
And the Harvest was devine.

The harvest was devine!

The First Air-Raid

Young Billy never met his Grandad on his Father's side of the family. He died several years afore he was born in 1930. Granny lived with the family, so as he growed up Billy accepted her as a part of the household.

They became quite fond of each other but in a distant manner. She was tall and always dressed in a purple or black long frock. Stern in speech and demeanour, she was held in awe by everyone. Howsemever, she would take both Billy's and his brother's part if they misbehaved. "Don't be too hard on 'em," she would call if a ding o'the lug from father looked likely. She never completely interfered but was a kind of advocate for the boys' defence when she deemed it necessary.

So Billy liked to help if the old lady was having a day abed with a cold or the screws in her back. This condition became more common as the years passed. The Doctor called it Lumbago.

Leaning beside the table near Granny's bed was a walking stick. This she used to pass messages to the family below. For convenience, over the years a code evolved. Vigorous and rapid knocks meant someone come quickly. A walking stick nine, nine, nine call! Fortunately Billy only remembers this happening once when the hot water bottle cracked and leaked into the bed.

The stick was mostly used for less urgent signals. One tap made at about half minute intervals indicated Billy was required for a mission. Two taps given between a similar interval and his Mum was needed to help Granny wash, dress, or use the commode. When this routine was over Billy would be summoned to "empty the slops". The contents of bedroom ablutions were deposited into a white enamel lidded slop pail and then carried to the privy up the yard. In the depth of winter, if the path was frozen, the task could be hazardous. Then a candle burnt in the privy so that "dint froze up". It was amazing how even on the coldest day a candle seemed to make it cosy. The family accepted this outdoor office without question. The only indoor comfort being a "Jeroboam" under the bed for night use.

But Billy's concern for Granny was not completely altruistic. Market forces entered, in the form of sweets. On the bedside table where the walking stick ledged there were always humbugs. They were not the cheap sort sold by the ounce from large jars in a sweet shop. But an elegant tin of golden, cushion shaped humbugs whose centre eventually became a chewy, minty toffee mass. Sometimes there was a bonus. If they were stuck together in the tin Billy very willingly assisted by banging vigorously the side of the closed container. A few would be released but if lucky it would be possible to sneak two stuck together. Luckily, Granny never seemed to run out of humbugs. If her normal supply from Christmas and birthday presents, plus gifts from visiting relatives did not meet her need then more were purchased in good time.

It was a long while before it dawned on Billy that the man often talked about in the household yet no longer there was his Grandad. Referred to by everyone as 'Father', stories abounded concerning him. So much so that the lad felt he really new him almost as much as Granny. But Granny and Grandad seemed so different that at first he found it hard to imagine them married and living together as his own parents did. As so often happens their differing characters complimented each other and they had been a devoted couple.

Billy learnt that his Grandad had been a Grocer who lived for fun, food, and his family. He loved spratts which he fried for himself with one hand in his pocket. In his youth he had been given to roistering. Stories were told about him racing home from a hostelry at North Cove in a pony and trap.

He would go out to a local shop and buy the breakfast first thing in the morning. Bacon, eggs, ham, kippers, bloaters and smoked haddock might all figure on the varied menu. Toast and home-made marmalade always followed. Cereals were seldom taken except porridge in the bitterest winter weather.

He was a tremendous leg pull, full of pranks. His shop boy was once sent to the Butchers to "buy fat liver and ask for half a pound of lean lard to fry it in". His youngest son remembered being sent for an oxtail and to ask for it to be "cut as near to the neck as possible." On his way home he was requested to call in at the "off licence" and see if they had "any second hand Guinness going cheap". Sometimes if in a reflective or philosophical mood he dismissed everything as a "money getting game." Once when he had a disagreement with ecclesiastical authority he had retorted "there's too much of your religion and not enough Christianity."

He kept and tamed a large grey parrot in a cage, teaching it to mimic his own voice. A cellarman worked at the Grocer's shop called Oliver. It was not long before the parrot's cry of Oliver could not be distinguished from Granddad calling. Many a time Oliver descended the shop's steep cellar steps after carefully raising the heavy wooden hatch, replying, as he thought, to a call from his boss. Alas, only to discover the parrot had been placed in the bowels of the building. Poor Oliver, his cry of "it's that damned parrot" became frequent.

For all his jokes the grocer was liked by his employees and family. His first errand boy described him as "generous to a fault" which in the end almost led to his undoing. But he must have had the Suffolk steadfastness and stubbornness. His Grocer's business, like so many others, got into difficulties in the depression of the late 1920's. Such was his character he did not relentlessly pursue his debtors. He sold out to his former shop assistant

who had, fortunately for everyone concerned, married a prosperous farmer's daughter. Grandad moved into a small cottage nearby and worked at his former shop to support his family. Billy's father however had to leave the college he was at and took a job at a wine merchants where whisky was sold to local farmers at three shillings and sixpence a gallon!

Billy wished he had the chance to chat with Grandad. But he had to be content with Granny and tales of her memories. There was an air raid warning in the first week of the war. By now Granny was in her eighties and took little initiative in household affairs. She was always slow to appear each morning and sat most of the day in her fireside chair. For all her long life she was never heard to utter an oath or use strong language. She puttered if anyone did. But as the wailing siren sounded in earnest during the night for the first time he suddenly saw why the two had been happy together. Her bedroom door quickly opened. With her veneer of stateliness and propriety removed she called along the landing to the household, "Come you on, Come you on, it's them buggers already."

The Choir Boy and The Toffees

We had a new young curate come to the Parish, and by that time I'd risen to be the second head-boy in the choir. Us boys were right thrilled by the arrival of this jolly young parson. The old Rector wasn't a bad old chap, but he didn't take much notice of us boys. So long as we sang the hymns and psalms in tune and sat quiet while he preached his sermon, he hardly seemed to notice us.

The young curate organised a lot of events for us boys. He formed a cricket team in the summer and we had trips out in the winter. The size of the choir grew and Sunday attendance was regular. One of the perks for being second head-boy was that I had a seat right next to this here young curate.

I told you he was a regular good sort. When we all sat down to listen to the fust lesson he always handed me a small toffee. Then we had another one second lesson and a third and final one at the sermon. If he was preaching or reading a lesson himself he always placed my toffee on the ledge by my hymn-book, so I never missed out. Well, the year rolled by and that got to Advent Sunday. We'd been practisin' Carols for a couple of weeks, so us boys were starting to get into the festive spirit.

I thought, he have been giving me toffees all the year, that will be nice on the next Sunday near Christmas to take him some. Now my pocket money only ran to a slab of creamy toffee. So I took that along and hid it in my cassock pocket. When the fust lesson come I took it from the cassock and showed the curate, trying to brake him a piece orf. Hard as I tried I wasn't able to. He looked at my efforts with amused sympathy. No doubt my boyish generosity had touched his heart.

"Give that to me," he whispered, "I'll sort that out in the Te Deum." He took it from me and hid it from the congregation's view in the palm of his hand. We all rose to sing. When the choir and everyone were going full pelt with the bit that go: "To thee all Angels cry aloud," he whacked the slab of toffee with all his might on the side arm of his pew. Startled, the poor old Rector opposite nearly shot out of his surplice. But he didn't know what it was.

The toffee was broken into pieces just right to eat. We both had a piece in the second lesson and then, as we shared another bit when the Rector's sermon began, the curate whispered, *"He has shown strength with his arm. And hath filled the hungry with good things."* No wonder us boys were sorry when this here young curate moved on to another parish.

November

November - no one seems to sing your praise;
And yet you have so much to give
With leaves of flame, and gentle sunlit days.

Quiet hours - despite unpleasant fogs;
And cosy evenings, time to meditate,
And tea before a fire of burning logs.

The curtains drawn - the family gathered round
The fireside, books to read, perhaps a TV play,
And from the night outside comes not a sound.

And on the farm - the harvest is fulfilled,
The wheat is stored, and fruit and nuts
Are gathered for our good against all ill.

A gentle walk - along a rural lane,
The silence that pervades the countryside
Are true delights, brought by November days
again.

Special days - All Saints, Guy Fawkes,
Remembrance Parades are seen;
Each bringing their own different thoughts,
And later in the month, Cecelia, music's queen.

So, November - do not let us cruelly malign
Your many blessings showered down
Like ripened grapes from off a bounteous vine.

Not a very favoured month I fear
Often 'lost' at backend of the year;
Very much maligned in every way
Everybody seems to think it grey.
Murky days are dismal, nights are long,
But often we may hear the robin's song
Encouraging us to 'take things in our stride'
Rejoicing as we look to Advent tide.

Brian Patrick

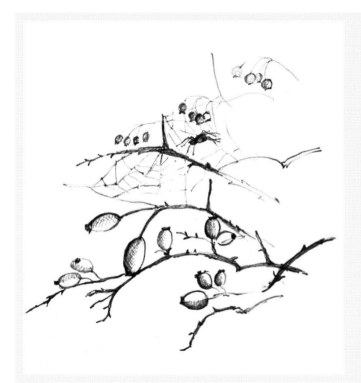

LAUGH WITH EPHRAIM

No hurry for Ephraim

Ephraim went to one of them there evangelical meetings held in a tent on the village common. The itinerate evangelist ended his address with an eloquent description of the fire and brimstone and purgatory awaiting those who did not mend their ways and compared that to the joy and bliss waiting in heaven.

With a final flourish he shouted, "Now my friends, stand up all those who want to go to heaven." Everyone stood up except Ephraim. "What," said the preacher, "Do you mean to say you don't want to go to heaven?"

"Well a course I dew," said Ephraim, "But not just yet!"

Wren and Heron Afore Christmas

Wren was saying to the Heron
As the Christmas hol's began.
"You look downhearted harnser
Whas up wi' you my man"
"Well! have you noticed brown bud?
I have, and find it hard
You never see a poor ole Heron
Pictured on a Christmas card.
There's Robins by the thousand
Singin' their lungs to bits
And mavishes and black buds
Or all the kinds of tits.
The other day I got a card
Wi' a hin on a heaap a muck
And a meadow with a pond
With every sorta duck.
There's comic ones with reindeer
And Santa Claus on his sleigh

The Shepherds round the manger
And the babe all warm in the hay".
"Things might be worse," say Wren,
"Some buds have a harder lot
You get Christmas cards wi' pheasants on
But on Boxing Day they're shot.
You still can fly on the marshland
All free and fresh and loose,
But Christmas is disastrous
For a turkey or a goose.
So cheer you up ole Harnser,
Preen yah feathers, join the festive fun,
No ones going to ring our necks
Or shoot us with a gun.
Keep you on my ole Frank
Don't be one to jib,
And I'll paint you a special card
Wi a Heron by the crib".

A Soldier for Christmas

It was the coldest Christmas I'd known. But then I'd only lived through eleven. Remembered perhaps five of them. All around was white, crisp and frozen when we broke up for the school holidays. It was 1942 and we were in the middle of 'The Hitler War.' The shops made valiant efforts to try and tricolate their windows and coach us into the festive spirit. And war or no war the holly and mistletoe were full berried that year. A sign of a hard winter they used to reckon. There wasn't much tinsel about. There was less of the material things but plenty of goodwill.

Mum and Dad asked me "What do you want for Christmas my man?" "I'd like a soldier," I say. During the war new toys were scarce, but a few cut out cardboard attempts were available. Mum was amazed at my wish for a soldier: "Don't you want some things for your toy farm yard?," she say. Oh I did have such a wonderful toy farm yard and animals. With a thatched barn and a cart shod. And I'd always make all my toy animals cosy and warm in the winter.

My favourite was a gret ole large black sow, made of lead. Bessie, I called her. I'd had her several years. She'd got a lot of dents, had lost half a leg and a bit orf one ear. Some of my friends said: "Hull that ole thing out." I wouldn't have done that for anything. When I did the imaginary feeding of the animals, I'd always give that ole sow an extra dollop of swill. And now in this cold winter I'd given her plenty of straw.

So my parents were rightly amazed when I asked "for a soldier." "I don't mean a toy soldier," I say, "I mean a real 'un. One of them soldiers from the Ack Ack and Searchlight batteries what come into town of an evening,

with medal ribbons on their tunic." They used to stand around in the market square, shuffling their feet around in the cold, waiting for the cinema or the pubs to open. Or 'haps on Sunday listening to the Salvation Army band. They had announced at school that folks were requested to invite a soldier home for "Christmas Tea". I thought this would be nice. My motive alas was not from a real zest of goodwill and beneficence. I just wanted to sit at the same table as one of the heroes who helped to drive the raiding bombers away.

The family wondered about this. What sort of chap would he be? "Good enough to protect us!" I say. But alas no more was said on the matter.

Christmas Day came. We had a gret ole cockerel father had fattened, followed by plum pudding. And I had my annual double lemonade. Then we all sprawled in the front room and dozed until we sat around the meal table again at 3 o'clock to listen to the King's speech. Afterwards Dad and Uncle Fred went for a walk: "To get an appetite for tea." I went back to the front room to eat roast chestnuts by the fire and look at my presents again.

Some half an hour later I heard Dad stamping the snow from his shoes on the pavement as he turned into our road. He allust did that. I went to the window. Between Dad and Uncle Fred walked a figure clad in a khaki great coat. Soon he was in the house. I stood speechless and garped at 'em, a lovely glow in my heart. I couldn't say a word.

Private Saw he was called. An army cook who made my Mum's Christmas because he loved her mince pies. Oh never have I enjoyed a Christmas Tea so much! As he left to join the Army lorry going back to camp, my Mum, who managed to see a joke in most things, say: "Glad to have seen you Mr Saw." Then after he'd gone she came up to me laughing and said, "I kept wanting to say 'glad to have sawn you Mr Seen!" I don't believe he would have minded.

Memories of over 50 years agone

In our family the routine for good health was basic, straight forward and easy to follow.

Get plenty of good wittles into you, keep your feet warm, dry and well shod and yer bowels open reg'lar. Whether these were particular Suffolk ways I am not sure. The majority of British households may have followed a similar routine in those days for all I know.

I remember my parents, grandmother and great aunts talking of some of the older country ways. The use of concentrated rhubarb juice as a purge had been common. In my childhood two dessert spoonfuls of Syrup of Figs was thrust down our reluctant gullets once a month on a Friday night. This unnecessary, unkind and possibly harmful assault on our "eternals" was

... a purge of rhubarb juice

nevertheless done with altruistic motives. Later in the forties and fifties a spell in a sick bay or hospital always meant on admission a dose of black-jack. This was a mixture of liquorice, senna and fruit extract. "Blas bor that wholly shifted yer!"

Keeping your feet warm and dry was essential for everyone's well being. No matter how shabbily some folks dressed, water proof boots and shoes were considered essential. I can recall at the infants school, the socks of the poorer children were placed to dry on the fireguards when they arrived on a wet and rainy morning. No conscientious teacher allowed any of the little ones in her care to sit in cold damp socks.

Sitting in damp garments was thought likely to spell disaster, a chill at least, pneumonia at worst. I remember seeing my grandmother hold a baby's napkin against a mirror to see it was properly aired. Strange because it was equally thought bad to molly coddle youngsters against the cold. Chilly bedrooms were quite in order.

I can remember ice on the inside of windows and even once on the bedroom water jug. Oh thank heavens for the joy and comfort of our feather beds! They were so thick you were able to sink right into them. By morning you were as snug as little Jenny Wren in her nest.

Good wittles were the final essential. Even when the shortages of war and rationing arrived we all fed well. Historical research has shown that overall the nation was better fed in wartime. There was less to go round, undoubtedly, but what was available was shared equally between rich and poor. Price of food no longer decided your diet as before.

Our household was not unusual in having three formal meals each day. Breakfast featured porridge, or a wheat cereal, suitably named as "Farmer's Glory" followed by eggs from our back yard hens. These were boiled, scrambled or poached and an omelette was made chance time to break the monotony. In the winter, when the poor ole hens were least productive my mum conjured up a somewhat leathery omelette from dried egg that had come across the Atlantic from Canada or the USA. Bacon, ham, mushrooms and fried tomatoes appeared for special occasions. We also had tinned sausages from the Dominions. The thick fat on the top of each can when opened was used for savory pastry making. Now and again my dad would proudly announce there were sweet-breads for breakfast. But the finish of the first meal each day was always toast and marmalade. Freshly ground coffee, at breakfast on Sunday, was our beverage - but tea was the normal drink during the week.

Whilst on the subject of tea and coffee, it is interesting to consider how attitudes have

"a good cuppa tea" for Grandad

changed. Only a few weeks ago I heard of a local doctor advising his patients to restrict their consumption of tea and coffee. Today the majority continue to enjoy both but do not consider it a health benefit. But in my grandparent's time a "good cuppa tea" was thought to "do yah a power a'good". When our son did not show a desire to drink tea we were happy for him to have other drinks. My father advised us "try and get him to have a good cup of tea". We are glad he didn't, for we are addicted to the tea-pot and for good or ill it provides much comfort and solace.

The ritual for tea brewing varied in different households and in many it still continues. But the common present habit of a tea-bag "copt" into a beaker of boiling water would have been unheard of fifty years agone. Making tea has a soothing effect on the preparer. My mum took care to warm the pot and always boiled freshly drawn water. The tea-pot was taken to the kettle, even if boiled on the open living-room fire, ensuring the water was at boiling point when poured on the tea. Tea made properly was better for you. As children, our tea was sweet, never too strong, and with rather more milk added than present day beverages. A cup of very sweet tea was a common cure following a mild shock or injury. I was given one after loosing a thumb-nail in a school cricket match!

In spite of the war, midday dinner was a substantial meal. In rural Suffolk everyone who was able was "Digging for Victory" so a plentiful supply of seasonal vegetables was available. Present day dieticians' advice of five portions of fruit and vegetables daily was the norm for us. "But Yes! We had no bananas"! The meagre butcher's rations were delightfully supplemented by our own home produced rabbits and poultry. No shortage of good gravy to "mix in with the 'taters."

Milk puddings, stewed fruit in season and custard kept us fully topped up for the walk back to afternoon school. Tea at five thirty was also formal. Two large plates of bread and butter (margarine thinly spread) coated with meat, fish

Granny enjoyed her mustard baths

paste or jam had to be eaten before we were allowed a slice of cake or home made biscuits. On Sunday sausage rolls and jelly, and in summer salad and tomatoes were an added luxury.

Tatterlegs were mum's special tea time treat - a type of short cake with currants or any dried fruit or peel when available. I have never heard the term used elsewhere and have not found, as yet, anyone else using it. I hope we will be inundated with folks who have heard the term "tatterlegs".

My Grandmother and her sister (my Great Aunt) who came every Sunday for lunch, both told my mum some of the old cures and remedies that they knew of. Granny was very keen on taking a mustard foot bath when she thought a cold was coming or she got wet feet. It was also thought good to soak your feet or poultice a push or absey with salt water. Some folk used a hot clay poultice.

Salt water in a weak solution as a gargle to prevent and ease throat problems was still used in my early days. When there was a lot of diphtheria and sore throats during the first wartime harsh winter we all gargled in the school cloak room with it. Every child had to take a large old meat paste jar to school. The teachers then dispensed it to us from huge white enamel jugs. Forty infants gargling around ten sinks, a quartet at each, was quite melodic. I must not recommend any child to try it but it is possible to gargle to the tune of Three Blind Mice!

I heard tell, but thankfully never saw the method practised, of a means of drawing the core from a push or absey. When the offending lesion was ripe a glass bottle was warmed by the fire or kitchen stove. Then muffled by an old sock, with the patient suitably advised to grin and bear it, the neck of the bottle was held over the push's head. Legend had it the core of the boil popped out and into the bottle.

Dad also told us about methods of extracting teeth in the olden days that he had been told or read about. Readers of Parson Woodforde's diary will be familiar with the ordeal of tooth extraction in the eighteenth century when it was usually the job of the local blacksmith or any strong wristed parishioner. But Dad told of reading about a different, and one hopes, more humane method. A length of the strongest pike fishing line was tied round the offending molar. This was attached to an especially adapted

Dock

shot gun. The patient braced himself and the gun was fired into the air from an opened bedroom window and the tooth - we hope - flew into the heavens. Anyone like to try it?!

My Great Aunt told of a remedy she had heard to cure a small child's hernia. A large ash or willow sapling was split down the middle but not severed at the top or bottom. The afflicted child was then passed through the riven sapling, which was then spliced and bound together. As the sapling healed and rejoined the child's hernia was reputed also to heal.

Most readers will have heard of various methods to cure warts. Aunt Eliza had been told if you buried a piece of prime steak in the ground as it rots so the wart disappears. For my part, better to keep the wart and eat the steak. Early morning dew taken from a dry cow pat was also said to cure warts and remove freckles when applied.

The use of onions cooked in milk and eaten daily to treat or prevent colds was commonplace. Sometimes an onion was sliced in half, lightly salted, and as the juice oozed out it was applied to ease the torment caused by chilblains. Recently a friend from Walpole told me he always applies a freshly sliced onion to a bee or wasp sting. Dock leaves rubbed on nettle stings were said to soothe. An infusion of dandelion tea was used to purify the kidneys. My aunt told of a market gardener who at the turn of the century hawked his asparagus around the streets on a barrow crying, "As-sparra-grass - Good for the urine - As-sparra-grass!" Edwardian bedrooms with a jereboam under each bed would have given some credence to his claim. This particular aunt was eating asparagus most days - albeit tinned sometimes - when she was in her nineties.

It was said that chewing the tips of willow branches in leaf was a useful palliative for rheumatism and arthritis, known locally as "the screws". There is great medical credibility to this claim. Richard Mabey in his Flora Britannica tells us that infusions of willow bark were employed by country people in the olden

Willow

days as a remedy for chills, rheumatism and "the ague". It was thought that as willow was prolific in wet areas it might be good for ailments associated with the damp. It worked, and almost 100 years ago the salicylic acid was isolated from willow and meadow sweet, which also grows on the wetlands. Soon a synthetic form of the active ingredient, acetylsalytic acid, was prepared and aspirin, one of the most useful drugs in medicine, had arrived.

Another simple and effective prevention and treatment for flatulence and indigestion was always used by my grandmother and father. Hot water! After the main meal of the day, and at other times when the need arose, they would take about half a cup of hot water. As a child I thought it was horrible - but then I did not know what indigestion was. And to this day I'm not quite clear what it is, but have been told frequently "you'll know when you get it"!

When I had a "bronical" cold or a cough mum always rubbed my chest with camphorated oil. This was a most ticklish process and invariably ended with us both convulsed with laughter. A far better treatment for a cold.

Another exercise used was to encourage vigorous blowing of the nose. Nowadays I would think this would be frowned upon by the medical profession. Nose blowing was supervised

A camphorated oil rub

A good blow

by an adult. A large white rag or hanky was held across the nostrils and we were encouraged to blow as hard as possible. The success and power of the nose-blowing was measured in a most unusual way. Maybe it had something to do with our close proximity to the railway station and my mother's former employment on the railway. The first tentative nose-blow was greeted by the comment "that's only got to Brampton" - the first station on the Beccles-Ipswich line. "Try again - that's better, got to Halesworth that time. Have one more go. Another big blow. Well done! Got to Wickermarket (Wickham Market). Go to sleep now, tomorrow we'll get to Woodbridge"!

It was often thought to light up a "fag" in the sick room helped "kill the germs". Certainly, in my childhood, we did not recognise the harmful effect that tobacco smoke had. But youngsters were warned not to smoke because it might "stunt their growth".

Catterlegs as mother used to make them

Ingredients

Shortcrust pastry made with 8 oz. Flour

2 oz. Butter
4 oz. Granulated Sugar
4 oz. Sultanas or mixed dried fruit
Milk or egg to glaze.

Method

Roll out pastry to oblong $\frac{1}{4}$ inch thick. Cover top two thirds with 1 oz. butter. Sprinkle this with 2 oz. sugar. Fold bottom third up then top third down. Give a quarter turn and roll out again.

Repeat.

Cover top half of pastry with fruit then fold bottom half over to make a sandwich. Roll out to $\frac{1}{2}$ inch thickness.

Score top in diamonds. Brush with glaze. Cut into oblongs.

Bake on a greased sheet Gas Mark 6, 200°C, 400°F for 15-20 minutes until golden brown.

A Black-bird Sang in Autumn

A black-bird sang in the Autumn,
But not like he'd done in May.
'Cos an early daag cloaked the stubbles,
Least them not all burnt away.
As the sun's rays brightened the berries,
And purpled the coal black sloe,
He raised his head to the morning
And spied swallows all ready to go.
"'Spose you'll soon be winging for warmfer's?
And leaving the winter behind.
Time me and my maates the sparrers
Ha'ter live on what we can find.
Do you ever get tired, all that flyin'?
An' how come you never get lawst?"
"Oh! We just ha'ter go", say the swallows.
"Yah see, we carn't stand a frawst,
Somehow (by instinct) we get there,
Don't bother how long we take.
But to tell yah the truth, time we're got there:

Wings blas! They do wholly ache"
"Fare ye well swallows" say blackbird,
"But I'll stay and give Suffolk a song.
Happen there'll be a bird-table
So winter on't seem quite so long".

LAUGH WITH EPHRAIM

Timely advice

Ephraim and Willum were working in the fields far away from the farm. One morning Ephraim tuned up late. That same afternoon about half an hour before leaving off time he started packing up his things for the day.

Willum looked at his watch and remarked that it wasn't leaving off time yet.

"Oi know," replied Ephraim, "But I was allus taught that that don't dew to be learte twice in one day!"

Now Do You Keep A 'Larnin'

Another look at dialect, sayings and customs. Here's a little ole task for you. Read this poem by "Quill" written when he lived at Theberton in the 1860's. His book of dialect poetry was published in 1865.

'Harvest Cart' in Suffolk

Yow, Jack, bring them 'ere horses here -
Get this 'ere waggin out;
I think this weather mean to clear,
So jest yow look about!
Come, put old Jolly to, right quick -
Now then, hook Di'mond on,
(There chuck yow down that plaguy stick!)
An' goo an' call old John

John bo' the "Cart shod close" we'll try
(Get yow up on the stack);
I'm sure the whate's by this time dry -
Bring them 'ere forks here, Jack.
Blarm that 'ere chap! where is he *now*?
Jest look you here, my man,
If yow don't want to have a row,
Be steady, if you can.

Ope that 'ere gate. Wish! Jolly - Wo!
Cop that 'ere rope up, Sam;
Now I'll get down 'an pitch, bo'; so
Jump yow up where I am.
Load wide enough, mate - that's the style -
Now hold ye! Di'mond! - Wo-o!
Jack! - that 'ere boy do me that rile -
Jest mind yow where yow goo!

There goo a rabbit! Boxer, hi! -
She's sure to get to ground,
Hold ye! Now then bo', jest yow try
To turn them nicely round.
Don't knock them shoves down! Blarm the boy!

-You'll be in that 'ere haw!
That feller do me so annoy;
But he don't care a straw!

How goo the time? I kind o' think
Our fourses should be here.
Chaps, don't *yow* fare to want some drink? -
There's Sue with the old beer.
The rain have cleared right slap away,
An' if it hold out bright,
Let's work right hard, lads (what d'ye say?)
An' clear this feld to-night!

When you have read and understood this poem it will give you an idea of what it was like working in a Suffolk harvest field over 130 years ago. You will also see how certain dialect words were in common use. I was fortunate to work with horses in a harvest field years later in the 1940's. The pattern of farm work then was not much different. Thus when I was asked to read the poem for the first time in the 1970's I was able to make sense of it. Yet by then, the Suffolk harvest scene had changed almost beyond recognition. Today one person on a combine harvester and another with tractor and trailer carries the already thrashed grain to a large store in the farm yard. Only a few months ago I was asked to explain to a lady born in 1953 what a corn stack was and why we had them! How fortunate that "Quill" wrote his poem which so vividly paints a verbal picture of a Victorian harvest scene.

What can you larn from the poem? See if you had the same findings as me.

The first thing that struck me was that "Quill", in spite of the idyllic harvest scene he describes still shows the need for everyone to hurry up and get the harvest in. He implies that the weather had been unsettled. "I think this weather mean to clear so just you look about." At the end of the poem he begs every one to "work right hard" and "clear the feld tonight."

At the start of the day the command is "to put old Jolly to right quick. Now then, hook Diamond on." Jolly was the horse, undoubtedly a Suffolk Punch put in the harvest wagon shafts.

Fourses

Diamond was the trace horse in chain-harness hooked on to the wagon shafts in front of Jolly. This extra horse power would be needed to pull a heavily loaded farm wagon, especially if the weather had been wet and tracks and fields dauby in the Suffolk clay. "Quill" uses the dialect to tremendous effect in the third verse.

"Wish! Jolly - Wo!" His "Wish!" is more often written as "Wheesh!" A command for the horse to go right. "Wo!" cannot really be classed as a dialect word as it is a common and universal term to stop a horse.

"Cop the rope up" again is dialect. The rope was gently thrown to the man on the loaded cart. Secured on one side, he would then use it to absail safely to the ground on the opposite side. Then when the next empty wagon was brought by a boy from the stack-yard the men changed jobs so they all took a turn at the more energetic job of "pitching" the sheaves up to the loaders on the cart.

"Load wide enough, mate - thats the style" causes memories to come flooding back when read. It was imperative that the sheaves (shoofs) of corn were set out wide on the load. This enables them to be bound by other shoofs in the middle. There was quite an acquired skill in this. Too narrow a load meant too small amount carried to the stack, but if you went to far out it might just collapse on to the ground. In reality each load was a mini-replica of the main stack being built in the stack yard.

The wonderful cry of "Hold Ye" is heard in the poem. This was called by the boy who moved the wagon on in the field to the next group of shoofs to be pitched by two-tine fork (or pitch fork) up to the loaders on the wagon or morphrey. Imagine what dire results might occur if you were not warned when the horses were moved on. Many a time as a lad I was shouted at for not calling "Hold Ye!" soon enough.

The poem also tells us about the bonus for the workers of catching a harvest rabbit. "There goo a rabbit". But this lucky bunny ran down a burrow before the dog Boxer catches him.

Towards the end of the poem the harvesters stop for "fourses" and Sue's "old beer". This is one way harvest customs had changed by the time I worked on a farm. We stopped and had fourses or "farses". But our drink was always cold tea. This was without milk and strained of leaves to prevent it turning sour in summer warmth or becoming stewed. Always slightly sweetened and kept as cool as we could in the shade, whenever possible it was immersed in a pond or a "deek". Sometimes we might stop for a shandy at the local on our way home. But in Quill's time it was the custom to home brew beer in the farm cottages.

LAUGH WITH EPHRAIM

Bit of a Blow!

After a special organ recital in the village church by the school mistress the rector congratulated her just as owd Ephraim emerged from behind the organ blower.

"Yes, rector," said Ephraim, "I reckons we did well."

The school mistress promptly informed him that the success of the recital had nothing to do with his "blowing". "Anybody can do that," she declared.

That evening when the recital was repeated there were several occasions when the music faded and at one point even stopped. Afterwards Ephraim emerged from the "blowing" position.

"We didn't do so well ter nite, did we missus?" he said.

Other recent titles from

THE HOBBIES STORY
Terry Davy
Over 100 years of the history of a well
known fretwork and engineering company

MEMORIES OF NORFOLK CRICKET
Philip Yaxley
200 years of history of Norfolk Cricket

LARN YARSELF NORFOLK
Keith Skipper
A comprehensive guide to the Norfolk dialect

RUSTIC REVELS
Keith Skipper
Humorous country tales and cartoons

LARN YARSELF SILLY SUFFOLK
David Woodward
A comprehensive guide to the Suffolk dialect

MIGHTA BIN WUSS
Tony Clarke
The life story of Owd Jimma

KID'S PRANKS AND CAPERS
Frank Reed
Nostalgic recollections of childhood

LARN YERSALF NORTHAMPTONSHIRE DIALECT
Mia Butler and Colin Eaton
A comprehensive guide to the
Northamptonshire dialect